ICE AGE™
THE MELTDOWN

Popcorn
ELT
Readers

Meet ...
the animals from ICE AGE THE MELTDOWN™

In the last ice age, Manny, Sid and Diego lived in a valley. They were very good friends.

Sid is a giant sloth. He loves talking.

Sid

Manny is a mammoth. He's sad. He thinks that there are no more mammoths in the valley.

Manny

Diego is a sabre-toothed tiger. He's fast and strong.

Diego

Crash and Eddie are Ellie's brothers. They're possums and they love playing games.

Ellie is a mammoth, but she thinks that she's a possum.

Crash and Eddie

Ellie

Before you read ...
What do you think?
Who are Manny's friends going to be at the end of the story?

New Words

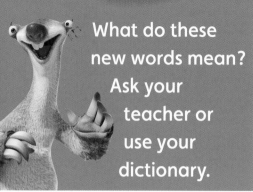

What do these new words mean? Ask your teacher or use your dictionary.

ice

The **ice** is very cold.

boat

Let's go in the **boat**!

melt

The ice is **melting**.

fight

The boys are **fighting**.

rocks

The **rocks** are very big.

safe

The cat is **safe**. The dog can't run after it.

swim

She can **swim**.

tree

This is a **tree**.

The ice age

The **last ice age** ended about 10,000 years ago.

valley

The house is in a **valley**.

way

This is the **way**.

'Come on!'

Come on!

Verbs

Present	Past
fall	fell
fight	fought
swim	swam

CHAPTER ONE
'We aren't safe here!'

It was a hot sunny day in the valley. The animals played on the ice and in the water. They loved the sun, but there was a problem ...

Manny talked to the animals. 'We aren't safe here,' he said. 'The ice is melting. Soon our valley is going to be under water.'

'What can we do?' asked the animals.

'There's a boat at the end of the valley,' said Manny.

'Is it far?' asked Sid.

'Yes,' said Manny, 'but it's safe there.'

'Let's go!' said the animals.

They all walked slowly to the end of the valley. Behind them, some ice fell into the water. Two big sea animals came out of the ice. They were hungry ...

Manny walked with his friends, Sid and Diego.

'Look!' said a young animal. 'He's the last mammoth!'

'I'm not the last mammoth!' said Manny. 'There are more of us!'

'Where?' the animal laughed.

Manny did not know. He was very sad.

'It's OK, Manny!' said Diego.

'You have us!' said Sid.

CHAPTER TWO
'She's the girl for you!'

Suddenly a girl mammoth fell out of a tree.
There were two possums with her.

'Hey!' said Manny. 'A mammoth!'

'Where?' asked the girl mammoth. 'I'm Ellie,
and these are my brothers, Crash and Eddie.'

'Why were you in the tree?' Manny asked Ellie.

'Possums like trees,' she said, 'and I'm a possum.'

'You are not a possum!' said Sid.

Ellie and her brothers walked with Manny, Sid and Diego. Ellie played with her brothers. They laughed and laughed.

'Ellie's funny!' said Sid to Manny. 'She's the girl for you!'

'I'm not the boy for Ellie,' said Manny. 'She likes possums, not mammoths!'

The ice was not very strong now. Suddenly the sea animals jumped out of the ice in front of them. Sid fell into the water. Manny fought the sea animals and they swam away.

'Wow! Thanks!' said Sid.

'Why did you do that?' Ellie asked Manny. She was angry.

'It wasn't safe! Soon there are going to be no mammoths in this valley!'

Ellie walked away.

Now Manny was angry too. 'I don't like girls!' he said to Sid. Sid laughed.

That night, they came to a tree. Ellie looked at it for a long time. Manny waited for her.

'I know this tree,' she said slowly. 'I was here when I was small. I didn't have a mum or dad. A possum lived in the tree, and she had two children, Crash and Eddie ...'

'Listen, Ellie,' said Manny. 'Crash and Eddie aren't your brothers. You're a mammoth!'

'The boy possums at school never liked me,' said Ellie quietly. 'Now I understand!'

'Well, I'm a boy mammoth and ...' Manny stopped suddenly.

'What?' asked Ellie.

'I like you,' he said.

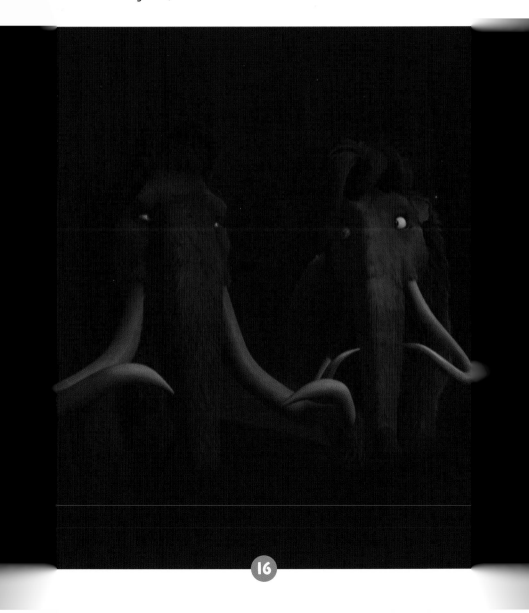

CHAPTER THREE
'I'm not going this way!'

Next day, the animals walked all morning.

'I'm tired,' said Sid.

'You're always tired,' said Manny.

'Look!' shouted Crash and Eddie. 'The boat!'

Everyone was happy.

'Come on! We don't have much time,' said Manny. 'The water is coming.'

Ellie stopped. 'I'm not going this way!' she said. 'It's not safe.'

'There isn't a safe way,' said Manny. He walked away quickly.

Ellie and the possums went a different way. They walked and walked.

Suddenly some ice fell and a lot of water came into the valley. They ran fast, but a big rock fell on top of Ellie.

'Ellie, are you OK?' shouted Crash.

'Yes,' she said. 'But there's no way out of here. Go and find help!'

Manny, Diego and Sid were near the boat.
Suddenly they saw Crash and Eddie.
'Come and help Ellie!' shouted Crash.
Manny ran after them, but he fell into the
water.

The sea animals were in the water too. They wanted to eat Manny.

The rock on top of Ellie was under water now. Manny swam to the rock. The sea animals swam after him and crashed. The rock fell and Ellie came out. She was OK.

CHAPTER FOUR
'Go after her!'

There was water everywhere in the valley.

'What now?' asked Sid.

'Look!' shouted Diego. 'The ice at the end of the valley – it's going to fall!'

The ice fell and the water went out of the valley. The animals were safe.

'Do you see that?' shouted Manny happily.

There were a lot of mammoths at the end of the valley!

'Let's go with them,' Ellie said to Manny.

'I want to stay here with my friends,' said Manny.

Ellie went to the mammoths. Manny watched her sadly.

'Manny, go after her!' said Diego.

Ellie walked slowly behind the mammoths.

Suddenly a mammoth fell out of a tree. It was Manny.

'Ellie!' he said. 'I want to be with you. Do you want to be with me?'

'Yes, I do,' laughed Ellie.

Sid and Diego were sad.

'It's you and me now,' said Sid.

Suddenly there was someone behind them. It was Manny! Ellie and her brothers were there too.

'Why are you here? Your friends are going!' said Diego.

'*You* are my friends,' said Manny.

'Friends are great!' said Sid.

THE END

Real World

ICE AGE ANIMALS

The world in the ice age

= under ice

USA

The last ice age ended about 10,000 years ago. In the ice age, a lot of the USA was under ice. What animals lived in the USA then?

tusk

Mammoths

O They were 3 metres tall.

O Their tusks were 4 metres long.

O They had a lot of hair so they weren't cold. Their hair was 1 metre long!

claws

Giant ground sloths

- They were 3 metres long.
- They sometimes walked on two legs.
- They had big claws.

Sabre-toothed tigers

- They were 1.5 metres long.
- Two of their teeth were very long.

teeth

★ **Which of these animals is your favourite? Why?** ★

Why did they die?

Why did these animals die? We don't know, but here are three possible answers.

★ There was a horrible disease.

★ Men hunted the animals.

★ The hot weather after the ice age was a problem for them.

What do these words mean? Find out.

world   die   possible
disease   hunt

After you read

1 Match the names and the sentences.

a) Manny

b) Eddie and Crash

c) Sid

d) Ellie

e) The sea animals

i) They are brothers.

ii) He's the friend of Diego and Manny.

iii) They want to eat Manny.

iv) Many people think that he's the last mammoth.

v) She loves Manny and Manny loves her.

2 Put the sentences in order. Write numbers 1–7.

a) A lot of water came into the valley. ☐

b) The animals walked to the boat at the end of the valley. ☐1☐

c) Ellie fell out of a tree. ☐

d) Manny helped Ellie. ☐

e) The sea animals jumped out of the ice. ☐

f) Manny helped Sid. ☐

g) Ellie, Crash and Eddie looked for a safe way to the boat. ☐

Where's the popcorn?
Look in your book.
Can you find it?

Puzzle time!

1 Find and circle six words from the story.

2 Find fifteen possums. Write the numbers.

a) There are ...four... possums behind the trees.

b) There are .... possums behind the rocks.

c) There are .... possums in the water.

d) There are .... possums in the boat.

e) There are .... possums on top of the rocks.

3 Where are they going? Follow the lines and write a sentence for each character.

Example: Ellie is going to the tree.

4 Follow Sid's instructions and draw the word.

~~S~~ ~~I~~ M D A ~~I~~ D S M M S ~~I~~ O ~~I~~ T D H

Cross out the letters in my name. Then find a word and draw it.

Imagine...

Work in groups of three. Act out the scenes.

A

Manny	Hey! A mammoth!
Ellie	Where? I'm Ellie.
Manny	Why were you in the tree?
Ellie	Possums like trees, and I'm a possum.
Sid	You are not a possum!

B

Manny	Do you see that?
Ellie	Let's go with them.
Manny	I want to stay here with my friends.
Diego	Manny, go after her!

Chant

1 Listen and read.

Did they like the ice age?

Ellie, Crash and Eddie,
Manny, Diego, Sid.
Did they like the ice age?
Yes, they did!

The mammoths were big.
The possums were small.
The weather was hot
And the ice was tall.

The tall ice fell.
A very sad day!
But Manny helped Ellie
And she was OK.

Ellie, Crash and Eddie,
Manny, Diego, Sid.
Did they like the ice age?
Yes, they did!

2 Say the chant.